Building Your Bounce

Simple Strategies for a Resilient You

A Journal to Support
Adult Resilience

Mary Mackrain and Nefertiti Bruce Poyner

with the Devereux Cent

The Devereux Center for Resilent Children
Villanova, PA
www.CenterForResilientChildren.org

Kaplan Early Learning Company
Lewisville, NC
www.kaplanco.com/devereux

©2013 The Devereux Foundation

Published by Kaplan Early Learning Company

Reprinted September 2013

ISBN: 978-0-88076-750-7

Kaplan Item Number: 29023

For more information on the Devereux Center for Resilient Children, visit
www.centerforresilientchildren.org or call (866) 872-4687.

Printed in the United States of America.

Editorial and Design: Abella Publishing Services, LLC

Table of Contents

Acknowledgments

A special thank-you to the Devereux Center for Resilient Children team and our publishing team members from Kaplan Early Learning Company and Abella Publishing Services for helping to make this resource come alive for adults everywhere. A special thank-you to Linda Likins, our dedicated leader, who wholeheartedly supported the development of this resource from beginning to end.

We would like to acknowledge the many leaders within the resilience and infant mental health field whose research and theory served as the impetus for this publication.

We are indebted to the families, teachers, and mentors who shared their stories and ideas, making this guide relevant and practical. Specifically, Mary dedicates her writing in loving memory of Sally Hruska, her infant mental health mentor, who taught her that healthy adults support the development of healthy children and within the context of these relationships comes strength, hope, and resilience.

And lastly, thank you to our loved ones who served as our protective factors throughout this journey.

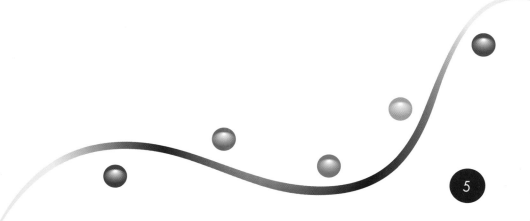

Introduction

All the wonders you seek
are within yourself.
–Sir Thomas Browne

As adults, we want to be happy and to achieve in life. But where do we start? Life comes at us and knocks us down at times. We have to pick ourselves up and keep moving forward. But how do we do that? You might know people in your own life who have faced great risk but continue to find success and happiness despite the odds against them. They have resilience, the ability to "bounce back" from misfortune or change. Resilient people tend to have something in their lives that helps them overcome challenges and move on in positive ways. The strengths that help resilient people bounce back are protective factors. Protective factors can be strengthened throughout life.

Faye, a music lover and great friend to many, has a serious illness and is enduring a year of chemotherapy. She deals with her illness one step at a time. She told herself she would be well through the entire summer outdoor concert series in her local community. She scheduled dates with friends for every concert. After each concert, she and her friends went out to celebrate with a dessert. She stayed well through the summer and got herself a new schedule of concerts for the fall!

William is the father of a son who is serving in the war. Every day when he wakes up, he thinks of his son, and every night before he goes to bed, his son is in his thoughts. William started a support group for parents whose children are serving in the war. They meet every week and share stories of fear, joy, frustration, and sadness. When his son calls, he is able to be present and listen to the words across the line because he has already dealt with his own emotions within the support group.

Johanna is a single teen mother of two young children. She is struggling to make ends meet and often feels lonely and afraid. Johanna is great with her children and often gets compliments from people in the community on her caregiving skills. Johanna went to a class on small businesses and decided to offer child care in her home. Word got out, and her child care business quickly became full. Johanna has made friends with many of the parents and often has play dates with her children and some of the families in her care. She is taking care of herself and her children.

Each of the stories above illustrates an example of a person who, despite the odds, bounces back.

The Devereux Center for Resilient Children (DCRC) has created a tool for adults that can help them strengthen their protective factors so they, too, can bounce back. We set out to focus on the adults who care for infants and toddlers because a strong, loving relationship between an adult and an infant sets the foundation for our youngest children to flourish and succeed in school and life. But as we progressed, it became evident that all adults could benefit from strengthening their protective factors. In today's world, we all face risk. Spending time

offsetting that risk by reflecting on and changing some of our behaviors can be of great benefit.

After careful review of the research related to adult resilience, we created the Devereux Adult Resilience Survey (DARS). The survey has 23 items, each one relating to thoughts and behaviors that have been shown to support resilience. Research[1] conducted on the DARS shows that it is an excellent tool for providing adults with an opportunity to gain valuable insights, particularly in the following four areas.

Relationships

The mutual, long-lasting, back-and-forth bond we have with other people in our lives.

Internal Beliefs

The feelings and thoughts we have about ourselves and our lives and how effective we think we are at taking action in life.

Initiative

The ability to make positive choices and decisions and act upon them.

Self-Control

The ability to experience a range of feelings and express them using the words and actions that society considers appropriate.

After you complete the Devereux Adult Resilience Survey (see page 10), this journal will help you understand more about these protective factors and how to strengthen your own relationships, internal beliefs, initiative, and self-control. Protective factors have an impact not only on ourselves but also on the people with whom we interact on a daily basis, such as our family members and co-workers. For example, if a caregiver for a group of infants is feeling good about himself, is able to express his own emotions, and has

---

[1] To review the research findings conducted on the DARS, please visit www.centerforresilientchildren.org.

good personal friendships and support, he will be more available and present with the children. The children, in turn, will greatly benefit from the love and nurturing and will be better able to share these skills later in life with other important people.

It takes a fair amount of reflection and practice to change any negative thoughts we might have and to integrate new behaviors that are good for us. You are worth it. Even if you are already a strong, happy person, you will want to continue building yourself up to maintain or increase your level of well-being.

This journal is your resource to help strengthen your resilience. Use it to reflect on all of your strengths. Reflect on areas you might like to practice as well. There are many strategies offered for you, so start small and choose one or two things you might like to try. This does not need to be done quickly. Behavior change takes time! Even after you feel some success with a new behavior, you can come back to a chapter and reflect on other things you might try, or celebrate the progress that you have made.

Best wishes on your personal journey.

> You must be the change you wish to see in the world.
>
> —Mahatma Gandhi

Devereux Adult Resilience Survey (DARS)

by **Mary Mackrain**

Take time to reflect and complete each item on the survey below. There are no right answers. Once you have finished, reflect on your strengths and then start small and plan for one or two things that you feel are important to improve. For fun and practical ideas on how to strengthen your protective factors, use the chapters in this book. For a free copy of the DARS visit www.centerforresilientchildren.org.

Items	Yes	Sometimes	Not Yet
Relationships			
1. I have good friends who support me.			
2. I have a mentor or someone who shows me the way.			
3. I provide support to others.			
4. I am empathetic to others.			
5. I trust my close friends.			
Internal Beliefs			
1. My role as a caregiver is important.			
2. I have personal strengths.			
3. I am creative.			
4. I have strong beliefs.			
5. I am hopeful about the future.			
6. I am lovable.			
Initiative			
1. I communicate effectively with those around me.			
2. I try many different ways to solve a problem.			
3. I have a hobby that I engage in.			
4. I seek out new knowledge.			
5. I am open to new ideas.			
6. I laugh often.			
7. I am able to say no.			
8. I can ask for help.			
Self-Control			
1. I express my emotions.			
2. I set limits for myself.			
3. I am flexible.			
4. I can calm myself down.			

How to Use the DARS and the Journal Contents

After you complete the Devereux Adult Resilience Survey (DARS) included in this guide, we recommend using a simple approach of (1) reflecting on all of your strengths—those items that you checked off as a "Yes"; (2) coming up with a few *goals* from the survey using those items you checked off as "Not Yet" happening; and (3) using the ideas in this journal to help you *strategize* some next steps. There are many strategies offered for you, so start small and pick one or two things you might like to try. For example,

> Ms. Davis, an infant/toddler teacher at Sunnyside Child Care, completed a DARS. When reviewing her results, she realized she had very strong relationships and positive internal beliefs about herself. She lives life with zest and loves to spend time with friends and family. Ms. Davis also loves to laugh and seeks out new knowledge, part of building initiative. Looking further at her DARS results, Ms. Davis noticed that the area of self-control had the most items checked off as Not Yets. Lately, she had felt easily frustrated, a bit tired, stressed, and had been more irritable than usual. She decided she wanted to focus on ways to calm herself. This would be particularly helpful in her work with young children, as she felt the infants could sometimes feel her tension when she held them. Ms. Davis looked in the Self-Control chapter of her *Building Your Bounce* journal under Item 4: I can calm myself down.

She found three simple strategies and decided the deep breathing exercise was something that she could practice every day in her classroom and at home.

Like Ms. Davis, we hope that you, too, can use this information to build your bounce.

Below is a simple tool that you may choose to use as you read through this guide. It helps you to remember your strengths as you identify your goals and strategies to improve. Best wishes on your personal journey!

Building Your Bounce Plan

My Strengths	My Goals	My Strategies
Relationships		
Internal Beliefs		
Initiative		
Self-Control		

Relationships

I've learned that people will forget what you said, people will forget what you did, but people will never forget how you made them feel.

—Maya Angelou

Relationships

Items	Yes	Sometimes	Not Yet
1. I have good friends who support me.			
2. I have a mentor or someone who shows me the way.			
3. I provide support to others.			
4. I am empathetic to others.			
5. I trust my close friends.			

Building Your Bounce Plan
Relationships

My Strengths	My Goals	My Strategies

Relationships

Relationships matter. "I've learned that people will forget what you said, people will forget what you did, but people will never forget how you made them feel." This quote by Maya Angelou highlights the importance of human relationships. Don't we all want to feel loved and to be able to love back? What is the payoff for having healthy relationships in our lives? Relationships support us in:

- Laughing more
- Feeling healthy
- Nurturing hope
- Feeling supported

- Having fun
- Sharing our emotions
- Being honest

There is no doubt that life can bring rough weather, but isn't it easier to weather the storms with a friend? You may have many strong relationships or maybe just a few. The number does not matter. What matters is what the relationships bring to your life. How do you maintain relationships? Take some time now to think about how you completed the relationships portion of the Adult Resilience Survey. Reflect on the items you checked with a "Yes" and those you checked with a "Not Yet." Use the strategies associated with each item in this chapter to get ideas for supporting your relationships.

> **DEFINITION**
> RELATIONSHIPS
> are the mutual, long-lasting,
> back-and-forth bonds we
> have with other people in
> our lives.

1. I have good friends who support me.

Supportive relationships pave the way for healthy, fulfilling lives. Relationships grow and strengthen through the course of life. By acknowledging and supporting the good, positive people who surround you, you create a safety net for yourself. Benjamin Franklin said, "If you want to make a friend, let someone do you a favor." Letting others help and support us is a gift to us and to them.

STRATEGY 1: Relationship Quilt

Think about what it takes to make a quilt. Years ago, it was common in some communities for groups to get together and work tirelessly to make a quilt for a cherished person. Similarly, relationships take time and effort, and when we cultivate them, they can provide us comfort like a warm quilt built with love, softening any challenge and enhancing our lives with a soft place to land. Take some time to think about the people in your life who surround you with comfort. What words come to mind when you think of these people or this person? Think of at least six words and create your relationship quilt.

Relationship Quilt

The people in our lives count. Take time to share some of these words with the special people or person in your life.

STRATEGY 2: Create a Want Ad

Do we always know what we need from another person? Sometimes we may find ourselves in a place where we don't feel supported, or maybe we move to a new place and do not have many good friends. Reconnect with what you want and need from a relationship in your life. Take time to create a personal want ad for a relationship.

HELP
WANTED

In a relationship, I need a person who is

_____

_____

_____

_____

I want a person in my life who accepts me when I

_____

_____

_____

_____

When I am with this person, I expect to

_____

_____

_____

_____

Take out this list once in a while and reflect on the information you generated above. Do you need more of this in your life? How might you go about it?

2. I have a mentor or someone who shows me the way.

A mentor is someone who offers support and encouragement to you in a specific area of your life. For example, maybe in school you really loved to write, and one of your teachers took time out to talk with you about your passion and supported your efforts to try new strategies and reach further in your ideas. Or maybe you have a grandparent who nurtured your curiosity for nature, taking you on field trips and nature walks. A mentor can be an important relationship. Mentorship can:

- Improve your self-confidence
- Increase your motivation
- Encourage optimism about future opportunities

Mentors might be in your life for a short time or for a long time.

STRATEGY 1: Mentor Tree

Think about people in your past who have helped you grow. Write their names on the spaces below.

_____

_____

_____

_____

_____

Mentors can be like branches of our life, helping us grow and move in new directions. Take time to appreciate these people as an important part of your life's development.

STRATEGY 2: Coffee Club

Imagine you are going to a coffee shop to meet with a new mentor. Imagine yourself walking into the coffee shop and sitting down at an empty table. You hear the door open, and you set eyes on your new mentor. What do you see?

_____

The person sits down, and you start talking. You are smiling. This other person is listening to you talk and then talks to you with a smile. What are you talking about?

_____

The meeting ends with a handshake and some laughter as you make plans to meet again. What are your hopes for the next meeting?

_____

Choosing someone to mentor us in life takes careful thought. We need to know what we want and why we want it. Remember, this person should inspire you.

3. I provide support to others.

Helping others is a benefit to them and to you. When you lend a helping hand or a listening ear to someone, you can experience increased energy and warmth. Supporting others can open our minds and can bring self-worth, greater happiness, and optimism. Even the smallest efforts can have great rewards.

STRATEGY 1: Choose a Family Member of the Week

Choose a family member of the week, and ask everyone else in the family to do special things for that person every day, such as make her favorite dessert, leave him a nice note on their nightstand, or give her extra hugs.

My family member of the week is

_____

STRATEGY 2: Thank-You Notes

Write a short thank-you note to a mentor or someone who has influenced your life in a positive way. Let her know how you are doing and what role she played in your life.

Thank You

STRATEGY 3: Pick Up the Mess

Helping others does not always have to involve direct one-on-one contact. Pick up trash at playgrounds, schoolyards, or other community areas to help the greater community.

Where will you start to pick up the mess?

_____

4. I am empathetic to others.

Empathy is when we accurately recognize and can understand what another person is feeling. It does not mean we feel the same way—that is sympathy. Empathy helps us to connect at a deeper level in relationships. According to psychologist Al Siebert, "Empathy is a survival skill."

STRATEGY 1: Empathy Check-Up

Think about a person you live or work with, and now imagine you are that person. Try to accurately describe how that person feels about living or working with you. A next step, if you feel comfortable doing this, is to ask that person how accurate you are. Are you indeed reading his or her cues clearly?

_____

_____

_____

_____

_____

_____

_____

_____

STRATEGY 2: Relating versus Debating

Next time you are listening to a friend tell a story about something that happened to him, make an effort to relate versus debate about how you are different. Relating to others can bring us closer.

Deep listening is miraculous for both
listener and speaker. When someone receives us with
open-hearted, non-judging, intensely interested
listening, our spirits expand.

–Sue Patton Thoele

5. I trust my close friends.

Trust begins at home. We can't control other people's reactions to our feelings and behaviors, but we can be aware of how their reactions affect us. When we have people in our lives who treat us well and give us positive feedback, we tend to trust them. Trust is a cornerstone of healthy relationships. When we trust a friend, we can be our silly selves. We can cry, and we can be frustrated. Sometimes mothers have said, "My child does fine at child care, but when he is around me, sometimes he just falls apart." We can learn a lot from children. They often show their true selves to those who love them the most, because it is safe.

With true friends, love does not waver because you are having a bad day.

STRATEGY 1: Reading Cues

If you have ever been a parent or a caregiver of a young child, you often can "read him like a book." Without words, you know when the child is hungry, sad, lonely, or in need of a break. You are reading cues—the verbal and nonverbal behaviors of the child. Part of building trust is having relationships in which you take time to listen and take in the verbal and nonverbal parts of communication.

Next time you are with a friend or your child, take time to focus on the cues that person is giving you. Is she telling you without words that she is interested in the conversation, or is there something she is doing to disengage? Reading cues helps to let the other person in your life know you care; she, in turn, can become more in tune with you as well.

> If you are trusted and people will allow you to share
> their inner garden…what better gift?
>
> —Fred Rogers

STRATEGY 2: Circle of Trust

Think about the people in your life you can tell anything to—the ones you call after a hard day and who listen without offering too much unsolicited advice. They are always there for you. Jot down the names of these people in the Circle of Trust below.

Remember that these people are special. These people will be with you through thick and thin. To strengthen and maintain trust, think about how often lately you have listened and been a support to the people in your circle. Do you need to reach out more?

Final Thoughts

Relationships bring joy and stability to our lives. Hopefully, you have spent some quality time reflecting on the people in your life. Come back to this chapter and revisit your responses and the activities as relationships grow and change as time passes.

 # Internal Beliefs

I believe that every person is
born with talent.

−Maya Angelou

Internal Beliefs

Items	Yes	Sometimes	Not Yet
1. My role as a caregiver is important.			
2. I have personal strengths.			
3. I am creative.			
4. I have strong beliefs.			
5. I am hopeful about the future.			
6. I am lovable.			

Building Your Bounce Plan
Internal Beliefs

My Strengths	My Goals	My Strategies

Internal Beliefs

When internal core beliefs about yourself are positive, they can serve as a cozy energy blanket around you. You can shrug off hurtful comments, accept compliments, and use your positive feelings to cope with life's ups and downs. It is never too late to start building yourself up. Positive internal beliefs lay a foundation for:

- Setting goals and sticking to them
- Learning from your mistakes
- Bouncing back from major life events and loss
- Accepting praise
- Trusting others
- Handling unexpected challenges
- Going with your instincts

How do you develop positive and strong beliefs? You can start by revisiting how you completed the Internal Beliefs section of your Adult Resilience Survey. Reflect on the items you checked with a "Yes" and those you checked with a "Not Yet." Use the strategies associated with each item in this chapter to get ideas for supporting your internal beliefs.

> **DEFINITION**
> INTERNAL BELIEFS are the feelings and thoughts we have about ourselves and how effective we think we are at taking action in life.

1. My role as a caregiver is important.

How you feel inside about your role as a parent or a caregiver of a young child impacts how you respond and relate to that child. In order to be as caring and responsive as our children need us to be, we need to be kind and nurturing to ourselves.

STRATEGY 1: Reflection: Caregiving Counts

Take a few minutes and find a quiet place. What are all of the things that you do in your role as a caregiver of a young child? You probably give lots of hugs, wipe noses, and clean up messes. What else do you do? List some of those things on the lines below.

_____

_____

_____

_____

_____

Now, take a look at your list of things you do as a caregiver, and think about what the positive payoffs are for you. What do you get out of your role? For example, if you give lots of hugs and comfort throughout the day to children, how does that make you feel? Do you feel loving, nurturing, joyful, and helpful? List some of the benefits of caregiving to your work below.

_____

_____

_____

_____

_____

There are only two lasting bequests we can hope
to give our children. One of these is roots,
the other, wings.

–Henry Ward Beecher

Caregiving counts. Your role in the lives of children is very important. Not only does caregiving bring safety and joy to children, it can bring benefits to you as well, every day. What we have to do is remember the benefits. How will you remember the benefits versus the barriers? Some simple ideas might be to:

- Take a minute to reflect on the benefits list you generated, repeating them out loud.
- Write your benefits on a sheet of paper and display it where you can see it every day.
- Use the Caregiving Counts sheet below. Write down your top four benefits and post the Caregiving Counts sheet somewhere important, or share it with a friend.

Caregiving Counts!

1. _____

2. _____

3. _____

4. _____

A hundred years from now, it will not matter what my bank account was, the sort of house I lived in, or the kind of car I drove. But the world may be different because I was important in the life of a child.

—Forest Witcraft

2. I have personal strengths.

As adults it is easy to think about all the things we want to change and make better. We can often lose sight of the good things that we already hold within. By recognizing and remembering our strengths, we can build ourselves up and use these strengths to solve problems.

Take a moment to answer these questions.

1. Do I tell myself nice things every day?

   yes _____ no _____

2. What do I fear might happen if I think good things about myself?

   _____

   _____

3. How do I feel when someone compliments me?

   _____

   _____

4. How do I describe myself?

   _____

   _____

These answers are a reflection of your ideas about self-strength. The more positive we become about our strengths, the better we are at counting on ourselves in difficult times and appreciating who we are all the time. When we exude strength, children feel more in control as well and trust that we can protect them.

STRATEGY 1: Making Time for Gifts

Take a few minutes to write down some of your talents and gifts. Are you a good singer? Do you like to dance or cook? What are you good at, and what do you love to do?

Gift 1. _____

Gift 2. _____

Gift 3. _____

Now estimate how much time each week you do each one of these three things.

Time on Gift 1: _____

Time on Gift 2: _____

Time on Gift 3: _____

If your time is more than 1 hour a week for each of these activities, good for you! You are giving yourself time to foster and enjoy your talents. If you are not spending enough time on your gifts, what can you do to bring these activities to the forefront? Start small. What is one thing you can do tomorrow?

I can _____

_____

_____ .

What is something you can do next week?

I can _____

_____

_____ .

STRATEGY 2: Counting Compliments

For one week, count every compliment that you get. Write them all down and put them in a special place, or write them here:

_____

_____

_____

When you reflect, think about how each compliment made you feel and how you responded. Do you see the same things in yourself that others see in you?

For one week, write down all of the compliments that you give other people. Remember why you gave the compliment, and think about what, if anything, you might be seeing in other people that could be an actual reflection of yourself. For example, if you say to another caregiver, "You are so good at reading stories to the kids," are you also good at reading to your own children or getting them engaged in fun activities?

Nice job on the presentation today!

Compliments count. Tell yourself one nice thing about you every day. If this does not come easily, put a sticky note on your mirror to remind yourself. Taking the time to practice positive messages in our own minds makes it come easier as time passes. Instead of saying negative messages such as, "Oh no, I forgot the milk again; I am always forgetting things," maybe you will say, "I did as much as I could do today; tomorrow I will make a list."

3. I am creative.

Creativity is a form of self-expression. It doesn't mean you have to be a good painter or a great creative cook. It means you find a way to express yourself openly and without judgment. The ability to create something from personal feelings and experiences can reflect and nurture our emotional health. It also helps us to nurture this type of freedom in our children. If you are open to expressing yourself and investigating the world around you, you can be better at supporting your children to do the same, or—better yet—you could do it together.

By taking time to fulfill your creativity, you may feel energized and understood, bolstering your internal belief that you are unique and special.

STRATEGY 1: Picture Poster

Take time to get to know what sparks your interest. Get a blank sheet of paper or a poster board, and gather some magazines or catalogs from around the house. Look through them and take out pictures that catch your eye. Do not put a lot of thought into this activity; just go with what attracts you. Glue all of your pictures onto the poster board or paper. Complete this activity before reading further. Reflect on what you created for a few minutes and ask yourself these questions:

1. Is there a theme? For example, do you have a lot of pictures of happy people? Maybe relationships or family is your theme.

2. What do you notice about the colors represented?

What can you do to bring more of these things—colors, themes, activities—into your daily life? If you are a teacher and you have pictures of bright flowers in your poster, can you bring a garden into your room? Can the kids create artwork with bright, beautiful colors for the wall?

STRATEGY 2: Solution Circle

Many of us face problems every day. We can practice using creativity to help us solve everyday hassles. Think about one problem you are having today. Use the Solution Circle below and write your problem in the center circle. Next, brainstorm new ways to solve the problem that you have not tried before. Don't worry if they seem unrealistic; just dream for a moment. Write the solutions in the solution circles.

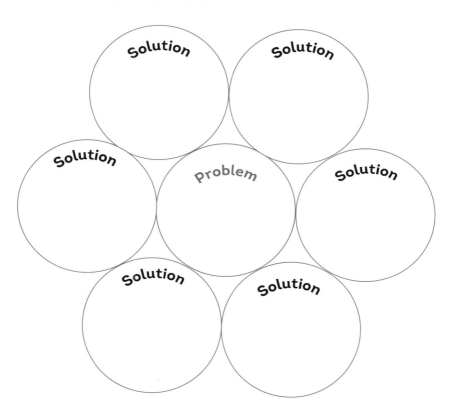

Now, think about these solutions. Are you willing to try one of them? Take time to talk with another person in your life about what you brainstormed. Take a chance and allow yourself to expand on your usual way of doing things. It will open the door to finding new possibilities for solving problems. When we can solve problems, we tend to feel more self-assured.

4. I have strong beliefs.

All adults face hardships. Somehow we need to find hope, peace, and gratitude in everyday life. This can take on many different forms. Some people have religion, others have a group of dear friends, and others have nature. It varies. Some have said that having meaning is the "bounce" in "bouncing back." A belief or faith in something in life gives people greater coping resources and resolve.

STRATEGY 1: Fostering Faith
Take some time to think about what you strongly believe in, and fill in the blanks below:

Thank goodness for _____ when something difficult or bad happens.

I could not live without _____.

I am most grateful for _____.

You may already feel that you have strong beliefs. If you do not, take time to think about the way you answered the questions above. Do these things in your life support your sense of peace and hope?

We are born believing. A man bears beliefs
as a tree bears apples.

–Ralph Waldo Emerson

5. I am hopeful about the future.

When you have a sense of hope, you have positive feelings about the future. You tend to look at life more optimistically. When negative things happen and you are feeling hopeful, you can more easily bounce back and look for ways to get the support and help you need.

STRATEGY 1: Share Your Story

You may have heard of the saying, "A problem shared is a problem halved." When life brings challenges and we share our fears and thoughts with someone we trust, we lighten our load. The person listening also benefits because he or she feels helpful and like a trusted confidant.

If you find yourself feeling restless or discontented about something in life, find a friend to share your feelings with and lighten your load.

Let us be grateful to people who make us happy;
they are the charming gardeners who
make our souls blossom.

–Marcel Proust

STRATEGY 2: Grow Your Gratitude

Gratitude helps us take notice of all the things that happen each day that are special and rewarding: when your baby smiles at you, when your kindergartner claims that you are the cuddliest mother, or when your teenager comes home to tell you about a 50-cent raise at the hamburger shop. These everyday moments are priceless, and when we pay attention and feel the gratitude, we are filled with joy. This in turns helps us to weather the hard times in life a little more easily.

> If you concentrate on finding whatever is good in every situation, you will discover that your life will suddenly be filled with gratitude, a feeling that nurtures the soul.
>
> **–Rabbi Harold Kushner**

What are you grateful for? Take time now to list a few things.

_____

_____

_____

_____

How does it make you feel inside to think of these things or the people you listed?

_____

_____

_____

_____

_____

_____

_____

Take a few moments each day to generate a mental or written list of two or three things you are grateful for. You can start a gratitude journal, keep a list by your bedside, or meditate during your morning cup of coffee—whatever works for you.

6. I am lovable.

When we are aware that people like and love us, it allows us to do thoughtful things for others. It also helps us to build relationships with someone— a parent, teacher, other adult, or friend—to ask for help, to share feelings and concerns, to explore ways to solve personal and interpersonal problems, or to discuss conflicts in the family.

STRATEGY 1: Opening Our Eyes

Think of people in your life who bring you happiness. Write down all of their characteristics. For example, are they good listeners, funny, empathetic?

_____

_____

Now put yourself in the shoes of these people, in their minds and eyes. Now look at yourself. How would they see and describe you?

_____

_____

Chances are, how they describe you is positive and loving. Can you see these things in yourself?

STRATEGY 2: "I Like Me" Book

Sit down with a child in your life and together create a book about the things you cherish in yourselves. Take turns creating pages and talking about what you love about yourselves. Use the book *I Like Me* by Nancy Carlson as inspiration.

Final Thoughts

Nurturing your inner self is important to your happiness and well-being. Take time to revisit the strategies in this chapter to check in on how you are progressing.

> Self-esteem is the immune system
> of the mind and of the spirit.
>
> —Lee Pulos

 # Go! Initiative

A person starts to live when he can
live outside himself.

–Albert Einstein

Initiative			
Items	**Yes**	**Sometimes**	**Not Yet**
1. I communicate effectively with those around me.			
2. I try many different ways to solve a problem.			
3. I have a hobby that I engage in.			
4. I seek out new knowledge.			
5. I am open to new ideas.			
6. I laugh often.			
7. I am able to say no.			
8. I can ask for help.			

Building Your Bounce Plan
Initiative

My Strengths	My Goals	My Strategies

 **Initiative**

Individuals with initiative:

- Are "go-getters." Each day, for them, represents an opportunity to take on new challenges and risks.
- Are excited about what today holds and look forward with great anticipation to what tomorrow will bring.
- Are often creative and can find more than one solution in a situation.
- Are often planners who carefully think through life's ups and downs and adjust accordingly.

As an adult in the lives of children, it is important to set an example of eagerness and curiosity that a spirit of initiative will bring. Initiative relates to adult resilience—faced with difficulty, those with initiative will make decisions and act upon them to move from a state of "what is" to a state of "what can be."

The time to begin thinking about improving (or maintaining) your initiative is now. Don't put it off for tomorrow. Take time to review your initiative items again, and use this chapter to begin building or renewing your level of initiative.

> **DEFINITION**
> INITIATIVE
> is your ability to make choices and decisions and act upon them.

1. I communicate effectively with those around me.

Reread the statement above, and this time underline the word *effectively*. It is the key word in the sentence. Many of us communicate often throughout our day. We communicate with those in our homes when we begin our day by saying good morning, and we engage in brief conversation over breakfast. We communicate with those in our neighborhood when we wave hello and wish them a great day. We communicate with those on our commute to work when a not-so-nice person cuts us off in traffic. Once we arrive at work, we communicate with co-workers, parents, and children. But if you were to replay all the different ways in which you communicate (and remember, we communicate both verbally and nonverbally), just how effectively are you communicating?

Consider the strategies below to help you better communicate with those around you.

STRATEGY 1: Seek to Identify

Is there one particular person with whom you find it very difficult to communicate? Write that person's name in the space below.

_____

Now, answer these questions.

Why do you find it difficult to communicate with this person? Is it because you feel that he will not listen to you? Is it because you have tried before and you feel the person did not hear you? Or is it because such strong feelings and emotions surface that you would rather just not try? Whatever the reason, spend some time reflecting in the space below.

_____

_____

_____

_____

I find it so difficult to communicate with this person because

_____

_____

_____

_____

STRATEGY 2: Communicate Using "I" Messages

In the last exercise, you noted some of the reasons you find it difficult to communicate with the person you identified. Moving forward, you may want to try the strategy outlined below when communicating not only with the person you identified but also with others as well.

When you communicate with others using "I" messages or "I" statements, you talk with them about a problem without accusing them of being the cause of the problem.

Consider this example:

Your co-teacher did not precut the materials for the afternoon art project as the two of you had agreed she would. You say to her, "You didn't cut the material for our afternoon art project!" While your statement is true, beginning the statement with *you* may immediately cause your co-teacher to become both defensive and maybe even a little angry. When communicating using "I" messages, you would instead say, "I was not able to help the children complete their art project this afternoon because the materials were not precut." Your co-teacher may then say, "I apologize. I completely forgot I had to cover in the preschool classroom this afternoon. I will cut the materials out this evening so we can finish the project with the children tomorrow."

You didn't cut the material.

I was not able to help the children because the materials were not precut.

Communicating using "I" messages will not solve all of your communication challenges, but it will make your communication sound less accusatory. Your message will be more effective.

STRATEGY 3: Put Pen to Paper

If you find it difficult to verbally communicate, another option is to put pen to paper. When using this approach, allow your thoughts and feelings to flow onto the paper.

You can send your thoughts via e-mail, text message, or U.S. mail. If you are not sure of what to say or how to say it, allow yourself some time to write your message. If your message has been written in a spirit of anger or frustration, set it aside for a day or two. After a few days have passed, reread the letter. If you are comfortable with what you have written, send it. If for any reason you want to make some changes, allow yourself to once again let your thoughts and feelings flow from pen to paper.

2. I try many different ways to solve a problem.

If at first you don't succeed, try and try again. For many of us, this is a lesson we were taught throughout our childhood. As adults, we may have strayed from this important strategy for building a more resilient spirit.

When we try many ways to solve a problem, we empower ourselves. Life will inevitably bring us many ups and downs. The key to making the best out of life is successfully managing our way through life's mountain highs and valley lows.

STRATEGY 1: Change Your Language

If you find yourself ever saying, "I can't," change this negative talk to something more positive. Try saying, "I am having a hard time with this." If you say, "I can't," this is the message you are sending to your brain. You can address your problems head-on when you face them with a can-do spirit as opposed to a self-defeating "I can't" attitude.

> Your living is determined not so much by what life
> brings to you as by the attitude you bring to life;
> not so much by what happens to you as by
> the way your mind looks at what happens.
>
> **–Kahlil Gibran**

STRATEGY 2: Listen to Your Inner Voice

Record yourself discussing a difficult situation you currently face. Replay the recording and jot down the number of "I can" and "I can't" statements or negative, self-defeating statements you use. If you find you used a great deal of negative self-talk, use this awareness to make improvements in your attitude regarding this situation or others that arise.

My Personal Recording

Number of I CAN statements _____

Number of I CAN'T statements _____

STRATEGY 3: Consider the Strengths of the Situation

When faced with a difficult situation or problem, it is hard to see the silver lining or the light at the end of the tunnel. Often, we make things even more difficult for ourselves by focusing on the negative.

Consider the following example:

> One bright and sunny morning, Isabel and her eight-year-old granddaughter, Nicole, woke ready to get their day started. They enjoyed a warm breakfast and then quickly prepared for school. On the way to school, they exchanged stories and laughs. Once at school, Isabel kissed Nicole goodbye and wished her a great day.

After stopping at the grocery store for a few items, Isabel headed home. When she was only about five minutes from her destination, another driver rear-ended her car. The impact caused the airbags to deploy and the front window to shatter. Isabel, shaken and worried, stepped out of the car. Police and emergency vehicles soon arrived at the scene. Isabel was taken to the hospital for evaluation and discharged after doctors reported a clean bill of health.

What is the problem?	The car has received extensive damage.
Identify the strengths of this situation.	Despite the impact of the crash and the extensive damage, everyone involved in the accident is okay.
What is the goal?	Work with the insurance company to decide if a. the car can be (or should be) repaired, or b. Isabel should begin looking into purchasing a new car.
What strategies will she try?	Visit local dealers in search of a new car.

In this example, it would have been easy to immediately focus on the negative—another person's careless driving and the damage received to the car. This negative focus, however, will not do any good. It may prove only to be more frustrating. By thinking through the strengths and goals of the situation, Isabel is ready to move on, and you will be, too, when you try this approach.

I am convinced that life is 10 percent what happens to me and 90 percent how I react to it. And so it is with you . . . we are in charge of our attitudes.

–Charles Swindoll

3. I have a hobby that I engage in.

You may be asking yourself, "Why should I engage in a hobby?" You may feel that you do not have time to engage in a hobby because there are not enough hours in the day. And you may also ask, "What does having a hobby have to do with building adult resilience?"

As you complete this activity, we hope you will discover that when you engage in a hobby, you release your passion. Released passion affects the children, parents, co-workers, and your family. In fact, when you pursue a hobby, you impact the world with your talents and gifts. Don't hide your creativity. Don't keep your skills only to yourself; use them to benefit others. This will make you feel wonderful on the inside.

STRATEGY 1: Identify Your Passion

Close your eyes for a moment, and think about those activities in life that make you smile or bring joy to your heart. In the space below, jot down the thoughts you have.

I love to . . .

_____

_____

_____

_____

We all have something in life that puts the sparkle in our eyes. Finding your passion takes time and effort. Take a closer look at what you have written above. You may have just uncovered your passion or your hobby.

> Don't ask yourself what the world needs.
> Ask yourself what makes you come alive, and go and
> do it. Because what the world needs is
> people who have come alive.
>
> **–Dr. Howard Thurman**

STRATEGY 2: Teach Someone Else

If you watch TV shows about cooking, home improvement, sports, or even talk shows, then you are watching someone living out their hobby. If you love to cook, then gather friends and family for cooking lessons. If you are a great gardener, then arrange to visit local child care centers and schools to demonstrate how to plant a garden. And don't forget a wonderful thing that happens when you pass along your knowledge and experience to others: You learn, too.

I would love to teach others about _____ .

STRATEGY 3: Think Things Through

Now that you are ready to add a hobby to your life, take a moment to reflect on the following questions to make sure you choose the best hobby.

- **How much time do I have?**

  Time-intensive hobbies like crafting ceramic bowls and pots are not practical for someone who only has a few hours a week to spare. If your time is limited, choose your hobby accordingly. And don't let your hobby become a source of pain, stress, or displeasure. You have added a hobby to make more of your life, not to burden it so that your hobby makes you unhappy.

- **How much money do I want to invest in my hobby?**

  A hobby doesn't have to cost a fortune to be enjoyable. If your hobby requires tools and additional items you are not prepared to purchase, renting some or all of your material/equipment is often a more practical alternative. You may want to try out the hobby for a while first to see if you plan to stick with it.

- **Do I like spending time indoors or outdoors?**

  If you choose an indoor hobby, you will not be affected by weather and you can enjoy your hobby from the comfort of your own home. For instance, you can carry out your cooking lessons in your kitchen and dining room. If you prefer an outdoor hobby, just look in your own backyard or a nearby park or playground. The possibilities are endless.

- **Do I want a hobby that I can enjoy by myself or with others?**

  Some people like to use their hobby time to enjoy precious solitude after a long day at work or after a full week of caring for their home and children; others prefer a more social hobby. If you prefer a more social hobby, check with local clubs, universities, churches, and community organizations to see what activities they offer.

4. I seek out new knowledge.

When was the last time you tried something new? As a caregiver or parent, you may find yourself growing tired of the same routine. By seeking out new knowledge, you reignite your spirit. Life will become more interesting.

STRATEGY 1: Take a Stroll through the Newspaper

Pick up your local newspaper or visit the paper's website. Scan the headlines. If you come across an article that interests you, read it. Maybe it is an article about schools and businesses in your area that are going green or an article about a new fashion trend. If any of these topics interest you, continue to learn more and read more about them.

STRATEGY 2: Subscribe to Professional Journals

If you are passionate about your particular field or are even thinking of a new endeavor, you might want to go online or go to the library to find professional journals in your area of interest. You can find the latest cutting-edge research. Journals can stimulate lots of new ideas and conversations.

I am interested in...

_____

_____

_____

_____

STRATEGY 3: Attend City- or State-Level Professional Development Conferences or Workshops

Look in the state or local section of your newspaper, which often lists seminars and conferences that are coming to town. Or visit the websites of

organizations that interest you to check for conferences. People from all over the world may come to present at state and local conferences. You learn not only from them but also from the more informal conversations you get to have with others in your field.

Conferences, workshops, or other events I am interested in are

_____

_____

_____

_____ .

5. I am open to new ideas.

There is one constant in life, and that is change. Day in and day out, you will be faced with change. When you embrace a spirit of resilience, you are able to adapt successfully to these changes. Resilient individuals are flexible and seek out new experiences and opportunities. And remember, when you are open to new ideas, new results may develop. After all, if you always do what you've always done, you'll always get what you've always gotten.

Closing your mind to new ideas is like living in a room with no doors or windows. Day and night pass you by, the sun rises and sets, and you miss out on beautiful opportunities. When you turn the knob and open the door, you allow the bright sunlight in.

STRATEGY 1: Learn to Think Outside the Box
Directions: In 60 seconds or less, connect the nine symbols below with four (only four) straight lines without lifting your pen or pencil from the paper.

In order to connect the symbols, you must go outside the box. Turn to page 53 of this journal to see how.

STRATEGY 2: Remembering to Remember

Think back to a time in your life when you resisted a change. You fought it and maybe even avoided it for as long as you could. Maybe one of your best friends was moving, and you didn't want to say goodbye. Or maybe as your first semester of college drew closer, you began to regret choosing a college far away from your family.

Write about a time when you resisted a difficult change.

_____

_____

_____

_____

Now, looking back and reflecting, what good came out of this change? Maybe you made new friends who are now your nearest and dearest, or maybe you reached out to family members for support, strengthening current relationships.

What positive outcomes did your difficult change bring to your life?

_____

_____

_____

_____

Remember that change can bring about positive outcomes. So, if you are in a work meeting in which some new ideas are being thrown around, you might consider them as opportunities for growth rather than detrimental proposals.

> Progress always involves risk: You can't steal
> second base and keep your foot on first.
>
> **–Frederick B. Wilcox**

STRATEGY 3: Opening Our Ears

Practice the joy of listening, engaging in uninterrupted one-on-one time with another important person in your life. Take time to call or meet with a friend and make it about them. Let them talk about their life without offering ideas or suggestions (unless asked to do so). This is not easy in today's world of quick fixes. If we put ourselves out there and engage in eye contact, read the cues of other people, and truly open our ears and listen intently, we will learn new ideas because our minds will be open and unencumbered by trying to manage other people's lives.

Who would you like to practice listening with?

_____

What will you do to be a better listener?

_____

_____

_____

_____

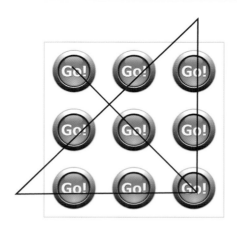

The answer for the problem
on page 51.

STRATEGY 4: Breaking It Down

New ideas are good, but too many at one time can shut us down. Sometimes it is good to take time to watch, listen, and wait for a good opportunity to take action—one that feels good inside and gets us excited to move forward. What are your good ideas right now that you want to accomplish? Which one is the most reasonable and manageable for your life today, as it is right now? For example, let's say that you want to take a new class on child development. That is a great idea, but some steps need to be taken to make it happen. Breaking down tasks into small pieces makes them more manageable and increases the odds of accomplishing them. Before taking a class, the first step might be to decide what topic you are interested in. Then you might go online to search the local colleges, looking at the times and days of the classes offered in your preferred subject. Consider whether the class is economically possible. Arrange child care if needed. Make an appointment with the instructor to see if the class is a good fit for you. Making a list of things to do and achieving each step helps us feel great once we get to the goal. What is a goal that you have?

Can you break that goal down into at least five manageable steps?

1. _____

2. _____

3. _____

4. _____

5. _____

Now, can you commit to starting the first step? If yes, when will you start?

Month/Day _____, Year _____

Writing down our commitment is the first step to making it happen.

6. I laugh often.

"Laugh, and the whole world laughs with you." One of the greatest joys we have is laughter. It is a marvelous gift that also releases chemicals in your brain that can enhance your day and reduce your stress. Laughter is a wonderful gift to share with children, parents, and co-workers. Laughter and a sense of humor have also proven to be great protection in times of difficulty.

STRATEGY 1: Bring in the Sunshine

Get a few co-workers, friends, or family members to join you in this strategy. With this strategy, the goal is to exchange a joke or funny story or situation each day that will make everyone smile. Once a week, identify the person who will post a joke, funny image, or story in a common area of your program. Bathrooms and kitchens make great places for this humorous addition.

> Laughter is an instant vacation.
>
> **—Milton Berle**

STRATEGY 2: Feel-Good Friday

One early childhood program in Missouri invites parents, staff, and children to participate in what they call Feel-Good Friday. On Fridays, the children and staff are encouraged to wear whatever they want (Yes, pajama tops and jeans have been worn to the center!). Spaghetti is eaten with a spoon, and ice cream is enjoyed with a fork.

What are your good ideas for a Feel-Good Friday?

_____

_____

_____

_____

_____

_____

STRATEGY 3: Comedy Club Preschool

Have you stopped today to listen to what the children in your classroom say and do? Every day can be a day at Comedy Club Preschool when you stop to listen to and watch the children you care for.

> Samantha, the caregiver for the three- and four-year-olds, went on a vacation to Kentucky. When she returned, she told the children all about her trip. "I've been to Kentucky," said one of the children. The caregiver, knowing that this child had never been to Kentucky, asked, "Are you sure you've been to Kentucky?" The child replied, "Yes, I love their chicken!"

> A mother was teaching her three-year-old daughter the Lord's Prayer. For several evenings at bedtime, the girl repeated it after her mother. One night she said she was ready to solo. The mother listened with pride as she carefully said each word right up to the end. "And lead us not into temptation," she prayed, "but deliver us some e-mail. Amen."

> Mrs. Murphy was busy carrying out a small-group activity with a few children when one child came running to her from the science area saying, "Mrs. Murphy, Brandon said a bad word. He said that bugs were in-sex (insects)." Mrs. Murphy briefly put her head down to hide her smiling face, then looked at the child and said, "Brandon is right, bugs are also called insects."

7. I am able to say no.

By now, you may have realized just how ineffective we are when we take on more responsibility and commitments than we can handle. Requests are made of us daily through phone, e-mail, letters, and in person. To stay productive and to get things done in a high-quality way, we must learn how and when to say no.

Remember, you cannot change others; you can only change yourself and how you respond. Others will continue to make requests of you; you have to set limits.

STRATEGY 1: DO, DELEGATE, STOP

There are many things in life we want to do, but there are only 24 hours in a day. Remember that you don't have to do everything. Some tasks can be delegated, some can be shared, and others can wait.

List those responsibilities you currently enjoy and would like to continue to DO.

_____

_____

_____

_____

List those responsibilities you could DELEGATE to someone else.

_____

_____

_____

_____

List those responsibilities that you no longer have interest in, are too difficult to attend to, and you wish to STOP doing.

_____

_____

_____

_____

STRATEGY 2: Before You Say What You Think, THINK!

The next time someone makes a request of you, instead of providing an answer immediately, tell the person you'll give her request some thought and get back to her. This will allow you to give it some consideration and to check your commitments and priorities. Then, if you can honor the request, great. But if you can't take on the request, simply tell the person: "After giving this some thought and checking my commitments, I will not be able to do what you have asked." By following this approach, you have given some consideration to the request and actually have thought about your response before committing yourself.

Who will you practice taking this approach with?

_____

_____

_____

_____

_____

You will either step forward into growth,
or you will step back into safety.

—Abraham Maslow

STRATEGY 3: If It's Not Working, Learn to Let Go and Move On

> If you were standing at a construction site and debris started to fall around you, what would you do? You would move, of course. You can't stop unwanted words and actions from occurring, but you can move out of the way.

Letting go and making changes may be difficult. Be willing to let go of situations over which you have no control to create positive change. If someone has unreasonable expectations of you, talk to him about it. If talking does not help, move away from those requests and, if necessary, that person. Take breaks from others who rob you of your energy and bring you down. Be willing to change and take small steps in a new direction.

If you are currently in a situation that is not working and you are ready to move on, take a moment to reflect in the space below, allowing yourself to begin the process of letting go.

Do I allow or permit others to influence me to do things that may not be in my best interest? The last time this happened was

_____

_____

_____

_____

I am ready to get away from people who use harmful words and actions that are not good for me.

The first thing I will do to let go and move on is

_____

_____

_____

_____

The second thing I will do to let go and move on is

_____

_____

_____

_____

Finally, in order to let go and move on, I will

_____

_____

_____

_____

- As a next step, photocopy the responses you just wrote, and place them in a self-addressed, stamped envelope.

- Seal the envelope and give it to someone who will mail it to you one month from the day you give it to her. Be sure to choose someone who will follow through and not forget.

- When the letter arrives, reflect on where you are in this journey of change. Did you follow the steps you outlined? Are you feeling better about being able to let go? Or do you need to start again in the process of letting go?

Breathe. Let go. And remind yourself that this very moment is the only one you know you have for sure.

–Oprah Winfrey

8. I can ask for help.

When you are not comfortable asking for help, you tend to suffer in silence. This attitude does not allow you to be the best person you can be. We suffer in silence when we experience difficulty in our lives and do not seek out help. Healthy initiative involves being able to ask for help when you need it. Remember, it's okay to ask for help. Don't be embarrassed, and don't worry about other people judging you. Asking for help when you need it shows strength.

Just think what might happen to you if you do not get help, or even better, what might happen if you do get the help you need.

STRATEGY 1: Trust Yourself and Others

Sometimes we just don't feel comfortable asking for help. Seek out individuals you trust and on whom you can depend. Also, trust yourself to make decisions that will be beneficial for you and your life.

Whom can you ask for help?

_____

_____

_____

_____

_____

STRATEGY 2: Ask and You Just May Receive

Take a moment to reflect in the space below. First, think about those things you are good at (e.g., working with families, planning social events). Then think about those areas in which you would like to make improvements (e.g., effectively managing your time, working with children with challenging behaviors). Now, think about where you could go for help to improve in the areas you have identified (e.g., friends, colleagues, classmates, library, the Internet).

What are you good at?

_____

_____

_____

_____

In what areas would you like to make improvements?

_____

_____

_____

_____

Where can you go for help to improve the areas you outlined?

_____

_____

_____

_____

STRATEGY 3: Post a Help Wanted Sign

A strategy used by a classroom teacher in Philadelphia may give you an approach to ask for the help you need. When this teacher was in need of help in her classroom, she would post Help Wanted signs with job titles people would be sure to "apply for." Take, for example, the Help Wanted: Hairdresser sign. The job responsibility of a "hairdresser" was to comb and wash the faces of the classroom dolls. Then there was the Help Wanted: Photographer sign. The job description of a photographer was to capture special classroom moments with a camera.

In order to get started using this strategy, visit your local hardware store or home improvement store to pick up a Help Wanted sign. Make a list of the different "jobs" you have, and post your available positions. You are sure to have many who will happily apply.

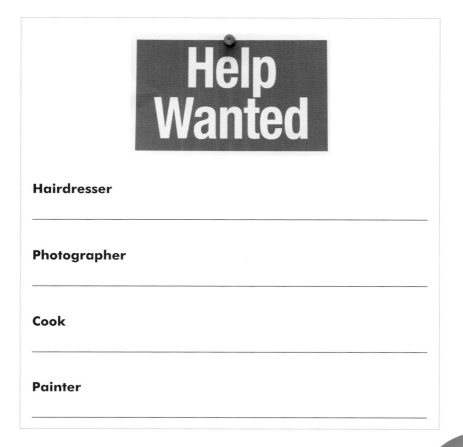

Hairdresser

_____

Photographer

_____

Cook

_____

Painter

_____

Go! **Final Thoughts**

Taking initiative in our lives is a skill that helps us bounce back and keep moving forward, trying new ways to solve problems and to stay curious and alive. Take time to celebrate all the ways you take action in your life, and revisit the items for initiative so you can continue your journey to resilience.

Self-Control

The ultimate measure of a man is not where he stands in moments of comfort and convenience, but where he stands at times of challenge and controversy.

—Martin Luther King, Jr.

Self-Control			
Items	**Yes**	**Sometimes**	**Not Yet**
1. I express my emotions.			
2. I set limits for myself.			
3. I am flexible.			
4. I can calm myself down.			

Building Your Bounce Plan
Self-Control

My Strengths	My Goals	My Strategies

Self-Control

Young children cry when they are hungry, smile when they are happy, and sometimes have tantrums when they are overtired. As we grow up, we learn to feed ourselves, continue to laugh and smile, and hopefully go to sleep when we are tired. It is important to authentically express our feelings, but sometimes we have difficulty. What do we do for young children to help them learn to express their emotions? We tend to label the emotions with words, acknowledge the emotions, and validate the feelings: "Sara, your face is frowning. Are you disappointed the ice cream is all gone?" We provide support along the way to help them through feelings. We can continue to do the same things for ourselves. If we do not, our emotions can begin to control our behavior. If we do, we can begin to feel more balanced and take time to read our bodies' cues. We breathe when we need to calm down, relax when we feel tired, and kick up our heels when we are happy and full of life.

Take time to reflect on how your self-control is doing. Remember, these answers are for you only. If there are a few areas you would like ideas on, keep reading and start taking action on your feelings inside.

DEFINITION
SELF-CONTROL
is the ability to experience a range of feelings and express them using words and actions that society considers appropriate.

1. I express my emotions.

For many of us, talking about feelings and emotions does not come easily. Emotions, however, are an important and valuable part of life. They guide us and connect us to others. Our emotions often give us energy and hope. When not channeled appropriately, our emotions can also cause us to behave in an inappropriate manner.

STRATEGY 1: Put a Label on It!

We often don't stop to think about how we express our emotions—we just do it. It can be very helpful, however, to name our emotions and to think about how we express them. For some of us, our emotions seem to get out of control. We may cry easily or get angry quickly, or we may sometimes become numb, unable to feel any emotions. Sometimes it's easy to name your feelings (e.g., happy, sad, loved). Sometimes you will find it harder to put a label on your feelings. When you find yourself having a hard time labeling a feeling, spend some time focusing on yourself and the feeling. Pay close attention to your body. Learn the different ways your body experiences different emotions. It can take some thinking, but it is helpful to name our feelings. Naming a feeling helps us understand it. Take a few minutes to reflect on the last time you experienced a strong emotion. What label would you use to identify this emotion?

The best way to label the last strong emotion I experienced would be to call it: _____ .

STRATEGY 2: Face the Man or Woman in the Mirror

Now that you have labeled the emotion, take a moment to reflect on where the feeling actually came from. What, exactly, has caused you to become so angry or frustrated? What, exactly, caused you to feel such joy?

The feeling of _____ (enter feeling from above)
I experienced was brought about because

_____

_____

_____

_____

_____

When you learn to acknowledge and label your emotions (and where these feelings come from), you begin to grow from the inside out. It is okay to become angry. What is not okay is expressing it in a way that will later be harmful to you or permanently damage the relationships you have with others. Practice recognizing and labeling your emotions. You will find yourself happier, healthier, and more in tune with your emotions.

> Music expresses that which cannot be put into words and that which cannot remain silent.
>
> **–Victor Hugo**

STRATEGY 3: Sing the Blues . . . If You Want To

An effective way to express your emotions can be by listening to music. Find songs that speak to how you feel. Pop, rock and roll, R&B, rap, country, and, of course, the blues all lyrically express different feelings and emotions you may be feeling. So find the songs that work for you, and sing your heart out.

> It'll never go away until the fear you are running from is finally embraced.
>
> **–Garth Brooks, "Face To Face"**

> Every chance you get, you seem to hurt me more and more, but each hurt makes my love stronger than before.
>
> **–Marvin Gaye, "Ain't That Peculiar"**

> I was the one with all the glory, while you were the one with all the strength. Only a face without a name, and I never once heard you complain.
>
> **–Gary Morris, Lee Greenwood, Bette Midler, "Wind Beneath My Wings"**

2. I set limits for myself.

It is important to be able to set priorities. The 21st century has come to mean constantly being on the go and trying to do it all without adequate time or support systems. Setting limits will help you restore and maintain the balance you need to be more emotionally healthy.

STRATEGY 1: Create a "One Day at a Time" To-Do List

If you don't write it down, it might not happen. So, instead of trying to remember to buy the eggs, pick up the dry cleaning, drop the dog off at the groomer, and meet your sister for lunch, begin your week by writing down the tasks you need to attend to—but take it one day at a time. Consider using the template below to help you set limits and take things one day at a time. Don't forget to check off the tasks you have completed. This will help you feel a sense of accomplishment.

My "One Day at a Time" To-Do List

Monday	Thursday
☐ _____	☐ _____
☐ _____	☐ _____
☐ _____	☐ _____
☐ _____	☐ _____
Tuesday	**Friday**
☐ _____	☐ _____
☐ _____	☐ _____
☐ _____	☐ _____
☐ _____	☐ _____
Wednesday	**Saturday/Sunday**
☐ _____	☐ _____
☐ _____	☐ _____
☐ _____	☐ _____
☐ _____	☐ _____

STRATEGY 2: Rest

Remember that the best bridge between despair and hope is often a good night's sleep. Without enough sleep, it is difficult to effectively deal with the stresses of daily living.

Tips for getting a good night's rest:

- Create a relaxing environment—is the room cool/warm enough? Do you need white noise?
- Exercise earlier in the day versus right before going to sleep.
- Keep a notebook next to your bed to jot down things that are keeping you awake.
- Develop a routine of going to sleep at the same time each night.
- Try reading a book before sleeping versus watching television— TV can stimulate the brain and keep you awake.

STRATEGY 3: Give Yourself a Time Out

Reflect on your successes. Give yourself time to daydream or spend time with a book or someone you enjoy. This time will help you reenergize and live life in a more meaningful and purposeful way.

Today, as I reflect on my successes . . .

_____

_____

_____

_____

_____

> As one person, I cannot change the world,
> but I can change the world of one person.
>
> **—Paul Shane Spear**

3. I am flexible.

Poet Maya Angelou was interviewed by Oprah Winfrey on Angelou's 70th birthday. Oprah asked her what she thought of growing older. Angelou said, "I've learned that no matter what happens, or how bad it seems today, life does go on, and it will be better tomorrow. I've learned that you can tell a lot about a person by the way he or she handles these three things: a rainy day, lost luggage, and tangled Christmas tree lights."

STRATEGY 1: The Power Is in Your Hands

Sometimes in life, we can't control what happens to us, but we can control what we will do about it. You may not be able to control everything that is happening in your life, but you certainly have the power to do something about it. You have the power to choose your response to life.

How will you choose to respond? Try laughter . . .

> Laughter gives us distance. It allows us to step back from an event, deal with it, and then move on.
>
> **—Bob Newhart**

Try asking others to help you adjust . . .

> Walking with a friend in the dark is better than walking alone in the light.
>
> **—Helen Keller**

Try being open to new ideas—you may like it . . .

> The most powerful agent of growth and transformation is something much more basic than any technique: a change of heart.
>
> **—John Welwood**

STRATEGY 2: Avoid Blame

It sometimes helps us feel better if we can blame someone else for the things in our lives that don't make us happy. Instead of taking time to place blame on someone else, why not take time and energy to focus on the solution? Remember, no one gets up in the morning and wants to do a bad job.

How will you take responsibility?

_____

_____

_____

_____

_____

STRATEGY 3: Laugh, Play, and Dance

Remember that joy equals energy. Sometimes a sense of humor is the best remedy for situations that create stress in your life. Seek out situations and people that make you laugh.

What places are fun for you?

_____

_____

_____

_____

_____

What people bring joy to your life?

_____

_____

_____

_____

Remember to . . .

> Work like you don't need money, love like you've never
> been hurt, and dance like no one's watching.

–Susanna Clark & Richard Leigh

4. I can calm myself down.

There are many techniques you can use to calm yourself down. Finding the strategy that works for you is what is most important. When you are not in a state of calm, this affects both your mental and physical health. In order to give full attention to the children in your care, it is very important that you take time to learn and apply strategies that will help you calm down and refocus.

STRATEGY 1: Your Safe Place

Think of a place where you can go to curl up and feel safe—a place you feel the urge to go to when things get tough. Is it an easy chair, a special room, a park? It is not always possible to go to this place when you are living life, but how could you create a representation that could follow you? Maybe your comfortable place is by the water where you can sit and sift through stones. You could find a smooth stone and carry that with you to hold during times of stress. Or maybe your safe place is your room where you have your favorite pillow or candles. Why not pack those things with you when you travel? We all need a place of solace to reflect on both good and hard times. What is your place?

Is it possible for you to go to this place more often to reflect on your feelings each day? If not, think about the characteristics of this place that you love and cherish. Is it the smell or the sounds? What part of this place could you replicate in your workplace or when you are away? Could you take a picture or take a memento? Take a few moments now and come up with an idea for how you might take your safe place with you every day.

_____

_____

_____

_____

STRATEGY 2: Practice Deep-Breathing Techniques

Deep-breathing strategies can help you return to a state of calm. It is important that you follow proper techniques to ensure that you get the maximum benefit.

Deep breathing involves:

1. Getting comfortable. It is best to wear loose-fitting clothes that will not hinder your movement.
2. Beginning breathing by inhaling the air slowly and deeply through your nose or mouth. Count to three.
3. Slowly exhaling the air through your lips.
4. Repeating the steps several times until you feel relaxed.

STRATEGY 3: Practice What You Preach

Mahatma Gandhi, who led the successful change to independence for India, advised his followers to "become the change you want to see in the world." Those words ring just as true today, many decades later. All too often, when a stressful situation arises, we try to change the person or the situation. This approach often leaves us feeling frustrated and even angry. But what if we were to make the change first?

Try the strategies below to help you practice what you preach.

- Use positive affirmations such as, "Life may be crazy, but I am calm!" Repeat this to yourself often in those moments of agitation or anxiety, or whenever you need help in returning to a state of calmness.

- Take time to privately relax, pray, or meditate. You may be surprised by the great peace and the will to go on that are brought about when you purposely focus on quieting your spirit without worrying about distractions of the world.

Final Thoughts

Self-control is an important part of resilience. In order to bounce back and get through life, we need the ability to safely experience and express a range of emotions. When we can do this, it nurtures our relationships with others and helps us to participate in life.

Conclusion

The experience of reflecting on your resilience and taking action to make some changes for yourself does not end here. Building resilience is an ongoing process. Life will bring uncertainty and joy, and when we are resilient, we begin to embrace it all and live life to the fullest. Be the resilient person you are meant to be, and keep building your bounce.

About the Authors

 **Mary Mackrain, MEd, IMH-E® (IV),** is a national infant and early childhood mental health consultant focusing on efforts to promote the social and emotional health, self-determination, and resilience of infants and young children and the adults who care for them. She also provides professional development and systems support in her home state of Michigan around early childhood mental health. She holds an Infant Mental Health Endorsement Level IV (Policy) through the Michigan Association for Infant Mental Health. Mary is also a National trainer and consultant for the Devereux Center for Resilient Children and coauthor of the *Devereux Early Childhood Assessment for Infants and Toddlers Program,* including the *Devereux Early Childhood Assessment for Infants and Toddlers, Devereux Infant and Toddler Strategies Guide,* and *For Now and Forever, A Family Guide for Promoting the Social and Emotional Development of Infants and Toddlers.*

 **Nefertiti Bruce Poyner** is an early childhood specialist and national trainer for the Devereux Center for Resilient Children. In her lectures, workshops, and trainings, she stresses the importance of social-emotional health and development in children. She is dedicated to educating parents, teachers, and administrators on the importance of paying attention not only to how our children perform academically but also to how they feel on the inside. Nefertiti is the coauthor of *Socially Strong, Emotionally Secure*, a publication designed to provide classroom teachers and parents with practical, easy-to-use activities to promote children's social and emotional health and resilience. She received her undergraduate degree from Virginia State University and her master's degree from Chestnut Hill College in Pennsylvania.

Notes

Notes